GHOST WORLD

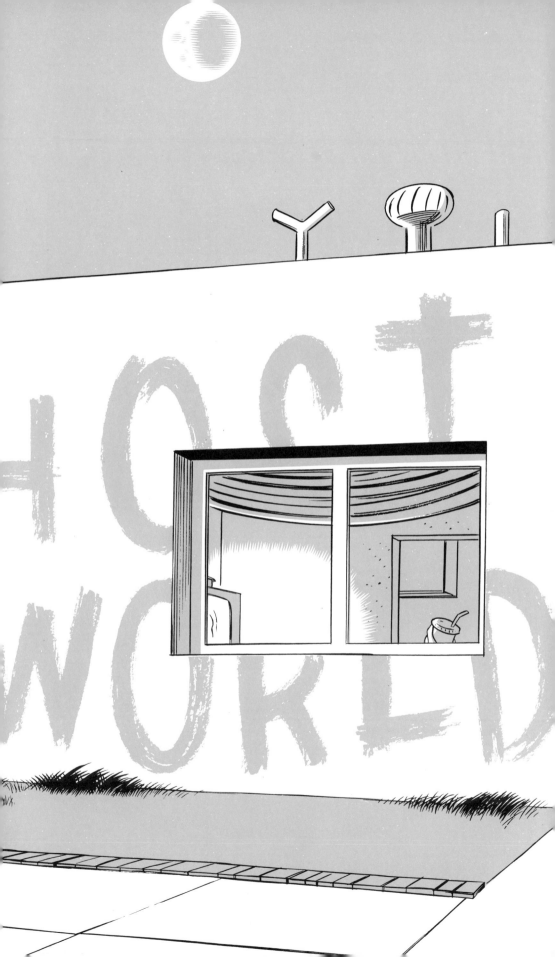

BOOKS BY DANIEL CLOWES

NOVELS

Like A Velvet Glove Cast in Iron
Pussey!

SHORT STORIES

Lout Rampage!
Orgy Bound

ANTHOLOGIES

The Manly World of Lloyd Llewellyn
#$@&!

for
Erika

Designed by D. CLOWES
Published by THOMPSON & GROTH
SPECIAL THANKS TO CHAS. SCHNEIDER

FANTAGRAPHICS BOOKS
7563 LAKE CITY WAY NE
SEATTLE, WASHINGTON 98115
LIBRARY OF CONGRESS CONTROL NUMBER 2014052341
ISBN: 978-1-56097-427-7

TWENTY-SECOND SOFTCOVER EDITION: FEBRUARY 2016

CONTENTS

GHOST WORLD

WHY DO YOU HAVE THIS?

WHAT?

I **HATE** THIS FUCKING MAGAZINE! THESE STUPID GIRLS THINK THEY'RE SO HIP, BUT THEY'RE JUST A BUNCH OF **TRENDY STUCK-UP PREP-SCHOOL BITCHES** WHO THINK THEY'RE "CUTTING EDGE" BECAUSE THEY KNOW WHO "SONIC YOUTH" IS!

YOU'RE A STUCK-UP PREP-SCHOOL BITCH!

CLICK

FUCK YOU! I CAN'T BELIEVE YOU BOUGHT THIS!

WAIT! SHH! SHUT UP! THIS IS THAT LAME COMEDIAN I WAS TELLING YOU ABOUT!

···HEHN-HEHN ··· MY FAMILY -- WHAT CAN I SAY? MY FAMILY MAKES THE ADDAMS FAMILY LOOK LIKE THE WALTONS!

HA HA HA HA

HEHN-HEHN

JUST BECAUSE I STILL LIVE WITH MY MOTHER PEOPLE THINK I'M PECULIAR··· SO WHAT IF SHE'S BEEN DEAD FIFTEEN YEARS!

HA HA HA HA

OH MAN, THAT'S SO PATHETIC··· IT'S NOT EVEN A JOKE.

I **KNOW**··· ISN'T HE **GREAT!** LOOK AT HIS SHOES -- IF HE'S SUCH A "WEIRDO," HOW COME HE'S WEARING NIKES?

...YOU'D BE SHORT TOO IF YOU HAD TO LIVE IN A FILE CABINET!

GOD, WHAT A LOSER!

I'M NOT WEIRD, I'M PRACTICAL --- HEHN HEHN YOU SHOULD SEE WHAT I SAVE ON RENT!

HA HA HA HA HA

JOEY McCOBB, LADIES AND GENTLEMEN!

CLAP CLAP CLAP CLAP

JOEY McCOBB!

CLAP CLAP CLAP

"JOEY McCOBB," HE IS OUR GOD.

I WANT TO DO HIM!

I BET! ACTUALLY HE REMINDS ME OF THAT ONE CREEP YOU WENT OUT WITH, THAT ONE SKINNY GUY WHO DRESSED LIKE HE WAS FROM THE FORTIES...

SHUT UP!

YOU ALWAYS GO OUT WITH GUYS LIKE THAT WHO HAVE SOME LAME, FAKE SHTICK...LIKE LARRY THE FAIRY -- WHAT A FOP! WHAT LOOK WAS HE GOING FOR -- A GAY TENNIS PLAYER FROM THE TWENTIES?

FUCK YOU! AT LEAST I DON'T WANT TO FUCK JOHN ELLIS!

EWWW! I HATE JOHN ELLIS!

...OH MAN, I FORGOT TO TELL YOU ABOUT WHAT HAPPENED YESTERDAY!

TV LOWDOWN

I WAS SITTING AT THAT RESTAURANT I WAS TELLING YOU ABOUT -- THAT PLACE "ANGELS" -- AND IN COMES JOHN ELLIS WITH THIS TOTALLY NORMAL-LOOKING OLD GUY...

...BUT... NONE OF US HAS ANY CONTROL OVER OUR PARTICULAR DESIRES, AND NOW, THANKS TO THE VERISIMILITUDE OF THESE COMPUTER-GENERATED IMAGES I AM ABLE TO ATTAIN MATERIAL THAT INDULGES MY SPECIFIC FANTASIES WITHOUT CAUSING HARM OR DAMAGE TO ANYONE...

HEY TOM, ENID'S ONLY EIGHTEEN!

FUCK YOU, JOHN!

GOD, WHAT AN ASSHOLE...

WHY DIDN'T YOU TELL ME ABOUT THAT RIGHT AWAY?

I WAS GOING TO, BUT I KNOW YOU THINK I HAVE A CRUSH ON JOHN ELLIS...

I DON'T **REALLY** THINK THAT... YOU DON'T, DO YOU?

DON'T WORRY!

...SO WHAT'S THE DEAL WITH HIM, IS HE LIKE A NAZI?

YEAH, I DUNNO... HE SAYS HE "HATES EVERY-BODY EQUALLY" BUT I KNOW HE WRITES FAN LETTERS TO MASS MURDERERS AND HANGS OUT WITH KKK GUYS AND STUFF...

GOD, HE NEEDS TO GET LAID!

YEAH, WELL... HE ASKED ABOUT YOU!...

SO HOW'S THAT REBECCA DOPPELGANGER? DOES SHE STILL ACT LIKE A STUCK-UP BITCH ALL THE TIME?

DOPPEL**MEYER**...

EVEN I'M NOT THAT DESPERATE!

OH YEAH, LIKE YOU COULDN'T HAVE ANY GUY IN THE WORLD IF YOU WEREN'T SO FUCKIN' **PICKY**... YOU'RE A SKINNY, BLOND WASP -- THAT'S WHAT EVERY GUY WANTS!

I'M NOT A WASP!

HEY, DID I TELL YOU ABOUT THAT SATANIST COUPLE THAT COMES INTO ANGEL'S?

I THINK SO...

THEY CAME IN YESTERDAY WHILE JOHN WAS THERE··· I DIDN'T WANT TO TELL JOHN ABOUT 'EM 'CAUSE FIRST OF ALL I FIGURED HE'D EMBARRASS ME SOMEHOW AND ALSO IT'S LIKE WHEN YOU TELL HIM ABOUT SOMETHING HE GETS REALLY **INTO** IT AND HE ACTS LIKE HE **OWNS** IT··· IT'S REALLY ANNOYING···

LIKE THERE'S NOTHING IN THAT STUPID MAGAZINE OF HIS THAT HE LEARNED ABOUT FOR HIMSELF --- IT'S ALL STUFF THAT OTHER PEOPLE TURNED HIM ONTO···

SO HOW DO YOU KNOW THEY'RE SATANISTS?

···YOUR ROOM LOOKS TWICE THE SIZE WITH CREATIVE MIRRORS···

IT'S **OBVIOUS**···

YOU REALLY HAVE TO SEE FOR YOURSELF -- THEY'RE **AMAZING**···

I SAT THERE AND WAITED UNTIL **FINALLY** JOHN ELLIS AND THE CHILD MOLESTER LEFT AND I TRIED TO DRAW THEM BUT IT'S IN MY BOOK AT HOME··· IT LOOKS **EXACTLY** LIKE THEM···

OH YEAH, SO GET THIS ··· WHEN THEY LEFT THEY BOTH HAD **UMBRELLAS** TO PROTECT THEMSELVES FROM THE **SUN** ··· THEY'RE LIKE TOTALLY **WHITE** ···

DO YOU KNOW THEM? DO THEY EAT HERE EVERY DAY?

THEY COME IN HERE FOR BREAKFAST AND LUNCH EVERYDAY···

THEY'RE NICE PEOPLE!

I HAVE MY OWN LITTLE FANTASY···

I LIKE TO THINK THEY'RE **BROTHER** AND **SISTER** SECRETLY MARRIED AND LIVING TOGETHER **INCESTUOUSLY**···

DUAL BREAKFAST
2 EGGS BACON PANCAKES $3⁹⁵

13.

WAIT... **WHO** SAID THAT?

SOME CREEPY DON KNOTTS GUY AT THE COUNTER... IT'S REALLY **TOO** INCREDIBLE... YOU **HAVE** TO COME WITH ME FOR LUNCH... WE HAVE TO FOLLOW THEM SOMEDAY...

OKAY, MAYBE...

...YOURS COMPLETE FOR ONLY $39.95, EXCLUDING CUSTOM TACKLESS INSTALLATION AND THICK, BOUNCY FOAM PADDING...

"OKAY, MAYBE..." ...**GOD**, YOU'RE **SUCH** A **DRAG!**

OKAY, OKAY!

NEXT, ON 'THE **NEWSBREAKERS**': GRISLY DETAILS OF THE **DOUBLE-SUICIDE** OF A REAL-LIFE **ROMEO** AND **JULIET**-- WAS IT AN ACT OF **LOVE** OR **SOMETHING MORE!?**

ALSO: MASS MURDERERS RECEIVE MAIL BY THE **TRUCKLOAD**, MANY OF THE LETTERS FROM **TEENAGE GIRLS!** LEARN THE SHOCKING TRUTH BEHIND "OUR DAUGHTERS AND WHY THEY LOVE THE **MEN WHO KILL**"...

Y'KNOW, JOHN ELLIS THINKS HE'S SO "OUT THERE" WITH THAT STUPID **MAYHEM** MAGAZINE OF HIS, BUT REALLY HE'S JUST INTERESTED IN THE SAME SH'T THE REST OF AMERICA IS INTERESTED IN!

I KNOW!

COMING UP NEXT: DOCTORS TOLD HIM HE WOULD **DIE** WITHIN THE YEAR. SHE WANTED TO **JOIN** HIM... WAS IT A DOUBLE SUICIDE OR A **DOUBLE-CROSS?**

WAIT, DON'T CHANGE IT...

...BUT FIRST, LET'S TAKE A LOOK AT THE FINAL RESULTS OF YESTERDAY'S VIEWERS POLL...

OH, FORGET IT... GO AHEAD...

1144

CLICK

CLICK

GOD, LOOK AT THESE STUPID CUNTS!

CLICK

Daniel Clowes

14.

GHOST WORLD

IT SAYS FIVE DOLLARS...

I KNOW, BUT I CHANGED MY MIND... I DON'T WANT TO SELL IT.

HOW MUCH IS THIS?

OH....THAT'S NOT REALLY FOR SALE...

Yard Sale

50¢

IT'S SO WEIRD... WHAT IS IT?

ISN'T THAT THE THING THAT DAVID LIPTON GAVE YOU IN FIFTH GRADE? I CAN'T BELIEVE YOU'RE SELLING THAT!

DON'T WORRY--I'M NOT!

OH NO...I SCARED HIM AWAY!

THAT'S OKAY-- I DON'T WANT HIM TO BUY ANY OF MY SACRED ARTIFACTS, ANYWAY... I CAN'T **BEAR** THE THOUGHT OF SOME JERK WITH A TRENDY HAIRCUT BUYING "GOOFIE GUS"!

AWW, BUT HE'S SO CUTE!

HE'S A FRUIT... OH MY FUCKING GOD! YOU WILL NOT BELIEVE WHO WAS HERE TODAY!

REMEMBER WHEN I TOLD YOU ABOUT THAT CREEPY GUY WHO THOUGHT THE SATANISTS WERE BROTHER AND SISTER?

YEAH...

HE CAME HERE AND TALKED TO ME FOR LIKE **TWO HOURS!** HE'S A **TOTAL NUT!**

HE KEPT TALKING ABOUT HIMSELF AND ACTING LIKE HE WAS GOING TO BUY A TON OF STUFF, BUT HE WOUND UP ONLY BUYING AN OLD EGG BEATER FOR TEN CENTS!

NOW WAIT, WHO IS THIS GUY?

GOD, YOU NEVER LISTEN TO ME! YOU KNOW THAT SATANIST COUPLE I'M ALWAYS TELLING YOU ABOUT? WELL REMEMBER HOW I TOLD YOU ABOUT THIS CREEPY OLD GUY AT ANGEL'S WHO THOUGHT THEY WERE BROTHER AND SISTER? WELL **THAT'S** WHO WAS HERE!

OH YEAH...

HE'S LIKE THIS GRISLY, OLD **CON MAN**... LIKE DON KNOTTS WITH A HOMELESS TAN... **BOB SKEETES**--THAT'S WHAT HIS NAME IS!

THIS IS A VERY FINE VOLUME INDEED! IT BETRAYS THE EXCELLENT TASTE OF IT'S SELLER! TELL ME: WHAT IS YOUR EXACT BIRTHDATE?

UMM... DECEMBER 23, 1979...

I THOUGHT SO-- **THE GOAT!**

HE SAID HE WAS A "WELL-KNOWN ASTROLOGER" AND THAT I SHOULD CALL HIM FOR A FREE "READING"!

WHAT A COOL GIMMICK!

C'MON! LET'S GO OVER TO ANGEL'S RIGHT NOW -- MAYBE HE'S THERE! WE CAN WAIT FOR THE SATANISTS!

WHAT ABOUT YOUR STUFF?

FUCK IT-- LEAVE IT THERE! I DON'T WANT ANY OF THAT SHIT!

WE MIGHT BE TOO LATE FOR THE SATANISTS... WHAT TIME IS IT?

LIKE FOUR-THIRTY...

I HAVE TO GO TO THE STORE FOR MY GRANDMOTHER AFTER THIS... YOU SHOULD COME OVER TONIGHT...

WHAT ARE WE HAVING?

OH MY GOD--DON'T TURN AROUND!

HI, YOU GUYS! WHAT ARE YOU DOING HERE?!

WE LIKE IT HERE, MELORRA... WHAT ARE YOU DOING HERE?

I WAS ON MY WAY TO AN AUDITION AND I SAW YOU TWO SITTING THERE! I HAVEN'T SEEN ANYBODY ALL SUMMER... I FEEL SO OUT OF IT! WHAT HAVE YOU GUYS BEEN UP TO?

NOTHING...

I'VE BEEN WORKING FOR GREENPEACE FIVE DAYS A WEEK AND GOING TO AUDITIONS... DID YOU GUYS SEE MY COMMERCIAL? OH GOD, I'M SO EMBARRASSED!

YOU WERE IN A COMMERCIAL?

I'M IN A TV COMMERCIAL FOR HAMPTON HAYES! I KNOW, CAN YOU BELIEVE IT?! ME, WORKING FOR A RIGHT WING POLITICAL CANDIDATE! BUT IT'S GOOD EXPOSURE, I GUESS... RIGHT NOW I MIGHT BE UP FOR A PART IN "APARTMENT HOUSE"... DO YOU GUYS HAVE MY NEW NUMBER?

YEAH, I THINK SO...

OH MY GOD, DID YOU GUYS HEAR ABOUT CARRIE VANDENBURG?! IT'S SO SAD...

DID SHE MARRY THAT ASSHOLE FOOTBALL PLAYER AND HAVE A KID?

NO, SHE'S GOT A HUGE TUMOR ON HER FACE... I HAVEN'T SEEN IT BUT I GUESS THAT BEAUTY MARK ON HER CHEEK TURNED OUT TO BE CANCER! YOU GUYS SHOULD CALL HER! IT'S SO SAD!

JESUS...

WELL ANYWAY YOU GUYS, IT'S **GREAT** TO SEE YOU! CALL ME!

BYE MELORRA.

YEAH **RIGHT!** LIKE I'M GONNA BE NICE TO CARRIE VANDENBURG AFTER HER STUPID BOYFRIEND CALLED ME A DYKE!

I WOULD, BUT I'M TOO BUSY GOING ON "AUDITIONS"!

I **KNOW!** CAN YOU BELIEVE THAT BITCH? SINCE WHEN IS SHE A FUCKING **ACTRESS!**

WE'VE **GOT** TO SEE THAT COMMERCIAL!

NO KIDDING!

MY DAD USED TO TRY TO GET ME TO HANG OUT WITH MELORRA BECAUSE HE THOUGHT SHE WOULD GET ME TO BE MORE POLITICAL... I CAN'T WAIT TO TELL HIM ABOUT HER COMMERCIAL! THAT'S GONNA REALLY **BUM HIM OUT!**

GIANT

EXIT OPEN ENTRANCE

IF I GET THIS WILL YOU EAT HALF OF IT?

EWW... OH MY **GOD,** WILL YOU LOOK AT THIS-- IT'S TOTALLY **PORNO-GRAPHIC!** WHO DO THEY THINK THEY'RE **KIDDING!?**

NILLA WAFERS

Choco Choice Choco Choice

CHIP CHIPPS CHIPPS

ookies o'kookies

ARE THEY REALLY SO **DESPERATE** TO SELL COOKIES THAT THEY HAVE TO SHOW A **BIG DICK** GOING INTO A **CUNT** ON THE PACKAGE!?

SHHH! IF THEY WERE **HONEST** THEY'D JUST TAKE A PHOTO OF A **REAL** DICK AND--

SHHH!

'mallow TWEENS

LOOK! IS THAT WHO I **THINK** IT IS?

OH MY GOD!!

I CAN'T BELIEVE IT! WE ARE SO **LUCKY!** HOW DID YOU KNOW IT WAS THEM?

IT'S TOTALLY OBVIOUS!

I KNOW!

OH MY GOD, WE HAVE TO SEE WHAT THEY'RE BUYING!

RED DEVIL TACO SAUCE...

I'M GONNA GO LOOK... WAIT HERE! IF THEY SEE YOU, ACT NONCHALANT!

WHAT?

YOU HAVE TO SEE FOR YOURSELF... BELIEVE ME, IT COULDN'T BE BETTER!

OH MY GOD!

Lunchables
Lunchables
Lunchables
Luncha

...YOU MUST HAVE GIVEN HIM THE WRONG IDEA!

I TOLD HIM TO PUMP ME 'TIL I COULDN'T TAKE ANYMORE...

WHAT?

YOU GUYS! MY CAR WAS OUT OF GAS!

HA HA HA HA

IT'S LIKE, IF YOU HAVE GIANT TITS YOU HAVE NO CHOICE **BUT** TO BE A SLUT!

YOU SHOULD KNOW!

SHUT UP. I MEAN, CAN YOU IMAGINE BEING A HIGH SCHOOL TEACHER WITH HUGE TITS? LIKE WHAT IF MRS. NOYES HAD **MASSIVE, POINTY HOOTERS**? THERE'S NO WAY!

OR, LIKE, WHAT IF A WOMAN WITH HUGE TITS DECIDED TO RUN FOR PRESIDENT--

...YIKES!

WHAT?

DON'T LOOK...

HI BECKY.

WHAT THE **FUCK?** DID SHE SAY "HI BECKY"?

I-I THINK SO...

OH MY FUCKING GOD, DO YOU KNOW WHO THAT **WAS?** YOU'RE GONNA DIE-- THAT WAS **CARRIE VANDENBURG!!**

REMEMBER HOW MELORRA SAID SHE HAD **CANCER** OR SOMETHING...

AIEEEE!!!

SHHH!

LET'S WALK OVER TO NORA JOHNSON PARK... I BET BOB SKEETES HANGS OUT THERE SO HE CAN CHECK OUT THE HIGH SCHOOL GIRLS...

LET'S NOT AND SAY WE DID.

YOU'RE SUCH A FUCKING LAZY PIG!

23.

"...JOHNNY APESHIT..."

THE JOHNNY APESHIT? THE GUY WHO SPRAY-PAINTED "ANARCHY" ON YOUR DAD'S CAR? I THOUGHT HE WAS LIKE A SKINHEAD JUNKIE...

HE *WAS*... GOD, WHAT AN *ASSHOLE!*... I CAN'T BELIEVE HE SAW ME DRESSED LIKE THIS...

"MOMMY AND DADDY"... *FUCK HIM!*

HE WAS CUTE...

OH *PLEASE*... YOU'RE A TOTAL *MORON!*

I'M KIDDING...

SO WHAT'S *THIS* LOOK CALLED?,

IT'S NOT LIKE I WAS "GOING PUNK" OR SOMETHING... I'M NOT FUCKING *THIRTEEN*... ANYBODY WITH HALF A FUCKING BRAIN COULD SEE THAT I WASN'T DRESSED LIKE SOME *MODERN* HARDCORE ASSHOLE... IT WAS LIKE AN OLD 1977 PUNK LOOK... ...I'M SURE JOHNNY *SHITHEAD* IS WAY TOO MUCH OF AN IDIOT TO FIGURE THAT OUT!

I WISH I COULD JUST COME UP WITH ONE PERFECT LOOK AND STICK WITH IT... LIKE WHAT IF I BOUGHT SOME ENTIRE MATCHING 1930'S WARDROBE AND WORE THAT EVERY DAY...

THE TROUBLE WITH THAT IS YOU LOOK REALLY STUPID AND PRETENTIOUS IF YOU GO TO A MALL OR A TACO BELL OR SOMETHING... AND YOU HAVE TO ACT A CERTAIN WAY AND DRIVE AN OLD CAR AND EVERYTHING AND IT'S A REAL PAIN IN THE ASS!

GOD, DON'T YOU JUST *LOVE* IT WHEN YOU SEE TWO REALLY UGLY PEOPLE IN LOVE LIKE THAT?,

SEE THAT GUY... I SAW HIM AT THE POST OFFICE YESTERDAY. HE GIVES ME A TOTAL BONER!

HE'S LIKE THE BIGGEST IDIOT I'VE EVER SEEN!

YOU GUYS UP FOR SOME REGGAE TONIGHT?

OKAY, YOU'RE RIGHT, BUT LOOK BEHIND HIM-- IT'S THAT GUY FROM **THE PLATYPUSSIES**, THE BASS PLAYER WHO GOT KICKED OUT...

I **HATE** THAT GUY-- HE'S AN ANNOYING **CRACK ADDIC**... PLUS, HE'S ABOUT AS CUTE AS JOHNNY APESHIT!

FACE IT, YOU HATE EVERY SINGLE BOY ON THE FACE OF THE EARTH!

THAT'S NOT **TRUE**, I JUST HATE ALL THESE OBNOXIOUS, EXTROVERTED, PSEUDO-BOHEMIAN ART-SCHOOL LOSERS!

NAME **ONE** GUY WHO LIVES UP TO YOUR STANDARDS... YOU HAVEN'T SAID ANYTHING NICE ABOUT A BOY SINCE YOU GOT OVER YOUR BRUCE LEE OBSESSION!

I DUNNO... SOMEBODY LIKE DAVID CLOWES...

WHO'S THAT?

HE'S LIKE THIS FAMOUS CARTOONIST JOHN ELLIS SHOWED ME SOME OF HIS COMICS...

YICK! I HATE CARTOONS!

THESE AREN'T LIKE NORMAL CARTOONS...

STILL, I JUST HATE ANYBODY WHO LIKES CARTOONS...

WELL **FUCK YOU**-- AT LEAST HE ISN'T SOME **GUITAR-PLUNKIN' MORON!**

WHAT DOES HE LOOK LIKE?

GOD, REMEMBER THAT GUY WHO USED TO CALL ME UP IN HIGH SCHOOL... THAT GUY THOMAS.. HE USED TO CALL ME UP AND ASK ME A BUNCH OF QUESTIONS AND THEN HE WOULDN'T SAY ANYTHING AND I'D BE LIKE TALKING TO MY-SELF AND I COULD HEAR HIM **PLUNKIN' AWAY** ON HIS STUPID GUITAR IN THE BACKGROUND...

WHAT A **FUCKIN' CREEP!**

HE LOOKS LIKE **HIM**?

NO... I CHANGED THE SUBJECT TO GUITAR-PLUNKIN' MORONS... I ALSO THINK HE USED TO ASK ME QUESTIONS SO HE COULD JERK OFF TO THE SOUND OF MY VOICE!

WELL, LOOK WHO'S HERE... **SHALOM!**

FUCK YOU! SINCE WHEN DO YOU WORK HERE?

ZINE·O·PHOBIA

FOR REN

SINCE ALWAYS ON TUESDAY... **HI REBECCA**...

SHE'S PRETENDING SHE CAN'T HEAR YOU.

PENUS *2

THE MONKS + THE THREE GUNS

SHE THINKS SHE'S CUTE ENOUGH TO PULL OFF THAT STUCK-UP VIRGIN ICE-QUEEN SHTICK...

SHE IS.

I GUESS YOU WOULD KNOW!

HEY, SPEAKING OF LESBIANS, I JUST GOT THIS **INCREDIBLE** VIDEOTAPE FROM SOME GUY IN **MANITOBA**...IT'S LIKE A TENTH GENERATION DUB OF THESE TWO CANADIAN **BULL DYKES** DRUNKENLY **TORTURING** SOME HIGH SCHOOL JOCK IN THIS **ABANDONED SCHOOLHOUSE**...

MMM...

ZINE·O·PHOBIA
SPECIAL APPEARANCES

JULY 3 CANCELLED
5 MR. + MRS. DOG SHIT
6 DR. DEATH ZINE
10 DAN CLOWES · COMICS
11 HARVEY SID FISHER
14 SKIN GRAFT
ORE TANNY-WIGLET
MIT

...IT'S REALLY HARD TO SEE BUT THERE'S THIS PART WHERE IT LOOKS LIKE THEY **PEEL AWAY** THE SKIN ON HIS FINGERS AND **SCRAPE** HIS **BONY STUMPS** ACROSS THE **BLACKBOARD!**

MASS MURDERER CARDS

JEFFERY DAHML B CARDS

WHAT DID JOHN ELLIS SAY ABOUT ME?

HE LOVES YOU... IT'S SO PATHETIC...

HEY **LOOK!** IT'S THE **PANTS!**

I CAN'T BELIEVE THEY'RE STILL HERE!

YOU LOOK LIKE EDDIE MUNSTER...

YOU LOOK LIKE HOMER SIMPSON...

YOU LOOK LIKE JULIE ON THE MOD SQUAD...

YOU LOOK LIKE ZELDA GILROY...

YOU LOOK LIKE BOSLEY ON CHARLIE'S ANGELS...

WHO'S ZELDA GILROY AGAIN?

YOU KNOW... DOBIE GILLIS.

HEY! GUESS WHAT I FOUND!

BOB SKEETES
ASTROLOGY · PSYCHIC
...083

WE SHOULD CALL HIM!

OKAY, YOU DO IT...

WHY DO I ALWAYS HAVE TO DO IT?

I CAN NEVER KEEP A STRAIGHT FACE...

OKAY, OKAY ...WHAT SHOULD I SAY?

DOOT DOOT DOOT

ASK HIM IF...

SHHH!

HI, THIS IS BOB SKEETES. I'M NOT IN RIGHT NOW BUT IF YOU LEAVE A MESSAGE, I WILL CALL YOU BACK. I **WILL** CALL YOU BACK.

BEEP

LISTEN SKEETES, I'M **ON** TO YOU... I KNOW ABOUT YOU AND THOSE **SATANISTS**... I'VE BEEN WATCHING YOU AND I SAW WHAT YOU DID... I'VE SEEN YOU AT ANGELS, SKEETES... YOU'RE NOT FOOLING ANYBODY WITH THAT TOUPÉE ... I THINK...

BOOP

29.

... HALF THEIR LINE IS OUT OR ON I.R. ... THEY **GOT** NO RUNNING GAME ... IF THEY DON'T GIVE HIM TIME IN THE POCKET, THEY GOT NO OFFENSE **WHATSOEVER!**

HOW MANY POINTS DID HE GIVE YOU?

SIX AND A HALF. HE SHOULD CHANGE HIS NAME TO FUCKIN' **SANTA CLAUS!**

I HALF EXPECTED TO RUN INTO OL' BOB SKEETES OVER HERE...

WHERE'S HE BEEN AT?

I SEEN 'IM OVER T'LONNIE'S...

DO YOU GUYS KNOW BOB SKEETES?

BELIEVE ME, YOU DON'T WANT TO GET MIXED UP WITH SKEETES... HOW DO **YOU** KNOW HIM?

HE CAME TO MY GARAGE SALE!

I BET HE DIDN'T **BUY** NOTHIN'! HA HA HA

HI!

HEY! THOSE GUYS KNOW BOB SKEETES!

SO... HOW'D IT GO?

I DON'T WANT TO TALK ABOUT IT... YOU WERE RIGHT!

...THERE WAS **NOBODY** THERE AND HE WAS LIKE THIS OLD **PERV**...

ADMIT IT, YOU REALLY **DO** HATE ALL MEN.!

MAYBE I DO.

OH MAN, THAT WAS **INTENSE** --

"INTENSE"?

SHUT UP! THOSE REDNECK GUYS WERE FRIENDS WITH **BOB SKEETES!** THEY WERE SUPPOSED TO MEET HIM HERE, BUT HE DIDN'T SHOW UP AND THEY GOT LIKE REALLY NERVOUS AND SAID SOMETHING ABOUT HOW SKEETES IS **DANGEROUS** AND I SHOULDN'T GET MIXED UP WITH HIM!

...YOU'RE NOT FOOLING ANYBODY WITH THAT TOUPEE ... I THINK ...

BOOP

LOOK HOW HOT WE ARE ... HOW COME NO BOYS EVER ASK US OUT ON DATES?

MAYBE WE **SHOULD** BE LESBOS!

GET AWAY FROM ME!

THE TROUBLE IS THE KIND OF GUY I WANT TO GO OUT WITH DOESN'T EVEN **EXIST** ... LIKE A RUGGED, CHAIN-SMOKING, INTELLECTUAL, ADVENTURER GUY WHO'S REALLY SERIOUS, BUT ALSO REALLY FUNNY AND MEAN...

THEN HOW COME THE ONLY GUY YOU EVER FUCKED IS THE **TOTAL OPPOSITE** OF THAT?

I KNOW... IT'S **FUCKED!** SOMETIMES I THINK I ACT SO STUPID BE- CAUSE I'M GOING CRAZY FROM **SEXUAL FRUSTRATION!**

HAVEN'T YOU HEARD ABOUT THE MIRACLE OF MASTURBATION?

I DUNNO... IT NEVER WORKS...

I ALWAYS WIND UP THINKING ABOUT MR. PIERCE...

31.

Okay, he's teaching summer school and his last class has just left and he's grading papers by himself...

Hello Mr. Pierce... Do you remember me?

Enid! I-I always DREAMED you'd come back!

I've thought about you EVERY MINUTE for the past two years!

No wait...

Wait... okay, I'm taking a shower...

He's so turned on he gets in with his clothes on...

No wait... okay, first he calls me up and says he's coming over...

Okay... he comes over and wakes me up in the middle of the night...

Enid darling...

No, wait... okay...

okay...

ZZZZ

Clowes

32.

GHOST WORLD

"YOU'LL NEVER GUESS WHERE I WAS TODAY..."

GUESS!

AT THE RENAISSANCE FAIRE!

NO, EVEN CREEPIER!

I DUNNO.

I WENT TO ADAM'S!

WHO'S ADAM?

YOU KNOW... "ADAM'S II"!

OH MY GOD! BY YOURSELF?

NO! THAT'S THE COOLEST PART! GUESS WHO I WENT WITH?

JOSH!

YES!

NO WAY...

I ABSOLUTELY SWEAR TO GOD!

I RAN INTO HIM AT THAT SHITTY RECORD STORE WHERE THERE'S NO PRICE ON ANYTHING, AND THEN WE WALKED AROUND FOR AWHILE AND WE WERE STANDING ON THIS TOTALLY RANDOM CORNER TALKING—

YOU MEAN YOU WERE TALKING!

—AND ALL OF A SUDDEN I'M LIKE "OH MY GOD, THERE'S ADAM'S!"

...BUT I HAVE NO INTEREST IN GOING THERE.

PLEASE JOSH... BECKY AND I ARE DYING TO GO IN THERE BUT WE CAN'T GET ANY BOYS TO TAKE US... PLEEEASE...THINK OF IT AS A SCIENCE EXPERIMENT...

ADAM'S II

ADULT BOO XX VIDEO

SALE % OFF

OVER 18

ARITA S

MILL

OMIGOD, JOSH... YOU HAVE TO LEND ME THE MONEY TO BUY THIS!

I'M COMPLETELY BROKE...

PLEEEASE JOSH ...YOU **HAVE** TO! I'LL PAY YOU BACK... **PLEEEASE!?**

SO WHAT WAS IT?

I'LL SHOW YOU TOMORROW... I'LL WEAR IT!

YIKES!

DON'T WORRY, IT'S NOT EVEN DIRTY AT ALL... IT'S LITER-ALLY THE **COOLEST!**

DO YOU THINK JOSH IS A VIRGIN?

OBVIOUSLY! TRY TO PICTURE HIM HAVING SEX! I BET HE DOESN'T EVEN **JERK-OFF**... HE'S ABOVE ALL THAT!

I GUESS YOU'RE RIGHT...

WILL YOU TELL ME YOUR LOSS-OF-VIRGINITY STORY AGAIN?

YOU KNOW IT BETTER THAN **I** DO!

LAST WEEK I TOLD NAOMI THE WHOLE THING IN **MINUTE DETAIL** AND SHE TOTALLY GOT INTO IT... IT WAS SO MUCH FUN!

YOU TOLD HER ABOUT ME AND MARTIN?!

NO, I MEAN **MY** STORY...I CAN'T KEEP YOURS STRAIGHT...

ARE YOU **SURE** YOU WANT TO HEAR THIS? ONCE I GET STARTED THERE'S NO STOPPING ME!

DON'T LEAVE OUT A SINGLE DETAIL!

OKAY, SO HERE I AM-- SWEET SIXTEEN AND NEVER BEEN KISSED AND **DYING** TO GET IT OVER WITH BUT ALL THE ELIGIBLE BACHELORS ARE LIKE TOTALLY SLEAZY CREEPS OR TOTAL **DORKS**...

HEY, IS **ALL** YOUR HAIR GREEN?

WAIT-- **REALLY** NEVER BEEN KISSED?

NO, NO.... I JUST MEAN I WAS STILL TECHNICALLY A VIRGIN.

HAD YOU EVER DONE **ANYTHING** WITH A BOY UP TO THIS POINT?

PRETTY MUCH EVERYTHING!

ANYWAY, SO THERE'S THIS SENIOR NAMED ALLEN WEINSTEIN. HE WAS LIKE THIS INTENSE, MOODY HIPPIE WHO SMOKED A **TON** OF POT AND LISTENED TO REGGAE (WHICH WAS A DRAG) BUT **THANK GOD** NOT THE GRATEFUL DEAD!

HE WAS **SUPER-RICH** AND PRETTY FUNNY, AND ONE TIME AT THIS PARTY WE MADE OUT... I LIKED HIM BECAUSE HE ALWAYS SEEMED TOO BUSY FIGURING OUT HIS COUNTER-CULTURE PHILOSOPHY (WHICH, OF COURSE, WAS TOTAL BULLSHIT) TO WASTE TIME WITH GIRLS... Y'KNOW WHAT I MEAN?

EVERYBODY JUST LETS THE MEDIA DO THEIR THINKING FOR THEM... THAT'S WHY YOU'LL NEVER HEAR ANY REGGAE ON THE RADIO!

AFTER THAT PARTY WE'D GO OVER TO HIS HOUSE AND MAKE OUT EVERY DAY UNTIL 5 WHEN HIS MOM GOT HOME. SHE WAS LIKE THIS TOTALLY CREEPY SHRINK WHO REALLY FUCKED HIM UP... THAT'S WHY HE WAS INTO ALL THAT STUPID HIPPIE SHIT, I THINK -- BECAUSE HE HATED HIS RICH PARENTS...

36.

AFTER ABOUT 2 WEEKS WE HAD DONE **EVERYTHING** BUT FUCK... WE'D ALWAYS JUST SORT OF STOP... I KEPT EXPECTING HIM TO PRESSURE ME BUT HE NEVER DID. I WAS READY TO TOTALLY **KICK HIS ASS** IF HE DID!

YOU BETTER SPLIT. I DON'T WANT THE BITCH TO COME DOWN ON ME TODAY...

ANYWAY, I FIGURE NOW'S THE TIME··· I MEAN, I WAS SIXTEEN AND EVERYTHING; THAT SEEMS TO BE THE AGE··· BECKY AND I PLANNED IT ALL OUT--SHE WAS MORE INTO IT THAN I WAS!

YOU **HAVE** TO WEAR THE PINK DRESS··· I'LL LEND YOU MY STOCKINGS!

THE BIG DAY WAS A THURSDAY···I MADE HIM DITCH SCHOOL AFTER LUNCH AND WE WENT TO HIS ROOM AND MADE OUT FOR A LONG TIME··· I ALMOST CHICKENED OUT BUT I KEPT THINKING THAT BECKY WOULD NEVER TRUST ME AGAIN. I THOUGHT ABOUT LYING ABOUT IT, BUT THEN I COULDN'T TELL HER WHEN I REALLY DID GET LAID···

THE TV WAS ON AND HE KNEW I WAS ON THE PILL··· I NEVER SAID ANYTHING LIKE, YOU KNOW, **'DO ME!'** OR ANYTHING. IT'S LIKE WE JUST KEPT GOING. HE GOT TOTALLY SERIOUS LIKE HE WAS TRYING REALLY HARD TO PLEASE ME BUT I JUST WANTED IT TO BE OVER. IT DIDN'T REALLY HURT AND I DIDN'T BLEED OR ANYTHING···

I REMEMBER **THE JEFFERSONS** WAS ON DURING THE WHOLE THING AND I ALMOST CRACKED UP A FEW TIMES··· I WAS TOTALLY AWARE OF EVERY LITTLE THING IN THE ROOM LIKE THAT, WHICH SEEMED WEIRD···

LET THIS BE A LESSON TO YOU, WEEZIE --DON'T **EVER** ASK ME TO DO ANYTHING NICE AGAIN!

AFTER IT WAS OVER, WE WATCHED STAR TREK IV ON CABLE WITHOUT SAYING A WORD. AFTER THAT I LEFT··· I SAID I WAS GOING TO CALL HIM WHEN I GOT HOME BUT OBVIOUSLY I NEVER DID···

ONCE I GOT OUTSIDE I STARTED TO FEEL REALLY WEIRD··· EVERYBODY WAS CHECKING ME OUT··· I KEPT IMAGINING BECKY'S REACTION TO EVERYTHING. ESPECIALLY THE JEFFERSONS.

ANYWAY, AFTER THAT I TOTALLY AVOIDED ALLEN AND NEVER ONCE TALKED TO HIM UNTIL ONE DAY I FIND LIKE THIS **TEN PAGE LETTER** IN MY LOCKER SAYING HOW MUCH HE LOVES ME AND EVERYTHING... I COULDN'T **BELIEVE** IT! IT TURNS OUT IT WAS, OF COURSE, HIS FIRST TIME TOO, EVEN THOUGH HE IMPLIED THAT HE WAS **SUPER EXPERIENCED!**

NOW I SEE HIM AROUND ALL THE TIME. HE'S OKAY, I GUESS... I'M NOT **TOTALLY** ASHAMED... SOMETIMES I WISH I'D PICKED A BETTER GUY, THOUGH...

DOESN'T **EVERY** GIRL!

YOU SHOULD HEAR **BECKY'S** STORY-- HER FIRST TIME WAS WITH THIS COMPLETELY FRUITY GUY SHE MET ON A **COMPUTER BULLETIN BOARD!**

OH **GOD**...

ARE YOU **SURE** YOU DIDN'T TELL HER ABOUT ME AND MARTIN?

GOD, YOU'RE SO WEIRD ABOUT SEX!

I AM NOT! I JUST CAN'T STAND HER!

YOU ARE SUCH A BITCH! YOU DON'T EVEN **KNOW** HER!

I CAN'T BELIEVE YOU WENT TO ADAM'S II WITHOUT ME!

The next day...

WILL YOU **PLEASE** TAKE THAT OFF!

HEH HEH ··· OUR SPECIALS TODAY ARE : **PASTA VASILIO**, WHICH IS A PASTA SALAD WITH A LIGHT BASIL VINAIGRETTE··

THAT WAS A POPULAR DISH IN THE FIFTIES, HUH WEIRD AL?

I IMAGINE SO! ALSO, WE HAVE A SPINACH TORTELLINI IN A TOMATO PESTO SAUCE. BOTH OF THOSE ARE $6.95... SHALL I GIVE YOU A FEW MINUTES TO MULL IT OVER?

I JUST WANT AN ORDER OF ONION RINGS.

··· I MIGHT ACTUALLY GET THE SPECIAL PASTA···

YOU **LOSER!**

♫ ···YOU'VE LOST THAT LO-VIN' FEELIN' ··· ♫

I HATE THIS SONG.

IT **SUCKS.**

WHAT DOES THAT EVEN MEAN?

WHO READS THOSE ARTICLES?

I **KNOW**···

OH **GOD**, I HATE THESE PEOPLE! PEOPLE WHO ARE **SUPER-SERIOUS** ABOUT POLITICS ALL THE TIME GIVE ME THE TOTAL CREEPS!

IT'S LIKE MY **DAD** ···I MEAN, WHO THE FUCK **CARES?!**

I KNOW, IT'S LIKE THAT GUY JASON·· IF YOU'RE NOT ALL **GUNG HO** ABOUT HIS SPECIFIC CAUSE, HE ACTS LIKE YOU'RE SOME TOTALLY SELF-OBSESSED **SNOB!**

" YEAH JASON, EVER SINCE YOU STOPPED EATING MEAT AND BATHING AND STARTED DOING GRAFITTI AND FUCKING UP ATM MACHINES, THE WORLD HAS BECOME A WAY BETTER PLACE ! "

STILL, I THINK IT'S KIND OF COOL THAT YOUR DAD IS LIKE THAT ···

IT'S DEFINITELY SOME PSYCHOLOG-ICAL THING··· IT'S NOT LIKE THESE ARE JUST GROOVY, CONCERNED PEOPLE WHO ACTUALLY **CARE** ABOUT HUMANITY ··· IT'S LIKE THE SAME AS WHEN GUYS ARE REALLY INTO SPORTS !

I KNOW··· OR COMPUTERS!

EXACTLY !

SO LIKE A WEEK LATER HE SHOWS UP AT HER WORK AND HE OPENS UP HIS SHIRT AND HE HAS THIS **HUGE TATTOO** WITH HER NAME AND LIKE HER **YEARBOOK PICTURE** ALL OVER HIS CHEST!

SHE WOUND UP KILLING HIM AND NOW SHE'S IN PRISON!

THAT'S THE CREEPIEST THING I'VE EVER HEARD!

HOW ABOUT IT LADIES... DESSERT? COFFEE?

"DESSERT"?! BACK IN THE FIFTIES WE CALLED 'EM **MINDBENDERS**, DADDY-O!

LISTEN TO WHAT SONG THEY'RE PLAYING!

♫ ...WHO'S BENDIN' DOWN TO GIVE ME A RAINBOW? EVERYONE KNOWS IT'S WINDY... ♫

THIS PLACE IS **GOD**.

...I REMEMBER WHEN I FIRST STARTED READING THESE I THOUGHT "DWF" STOOD FOR "DWARF"... I COULD NEVER FIGURE OUT WHY SO MANY **DWARVES** WERE PLACING ADS...

LEAVE A MESSAGE THIS TIME!

GOD, HE SOUNDS **SO** GAY!

MAYBE THE REDHEAD IN THE BLUE DRESS IS A GUY!

SHH!

HI DAHLING, IT'S **ME**... YOUR REDHEAD FROM CITIZEN KANE'S! I WAS SIMPLY **FLABBERGASTED** WHEN I SAW YOUR AD AND I'M **DYING** TO SEE YOU AGAIN! MEET ME AT A RESTAURANT CALLED HUBBA HUBBA IN THE VILLEVIEW PLAZA ON FRIDAY AT THREE O'CLOCK. I CAN'T **WAIT** TO SEE YOU, DAHLING... **CIAO!**

HA HA HA HA HA HA HA HA HA HA

WHAT SHOULD WE DO?

ONE OF US SHOULD PRETEND TO BE THE GIRL!

HE OBVIOUSLY KNOWS WHAT SHE LOOKS LIKE.

OH DUH!

GOD, THIS IS SO UNBEARABLE!

I AGREE!

YOU GUYS CAN BRING THAT UP TO THE FRONT WHEN YOU'RE READY.

IS HE STILL STARING?

GO AHEAD AND LOOK, BUT DON'T MAKE IT TOO OBVIOUS.

HE DIDN'T STICK AROUND FOR VERY LONG… SHE'S ONLY TWENTY-FIVE MINUTES LATE…

HE FIGURED IT OUT.

WHAT DID HE SAY?

IT LOOKED LIKE "VERY FUNNY".

IT WAS SOMETHING FUCK!

HEY AL, DID THAT GUY SAY ANYTHING TO YOU BEFORE HE LEFT?

NOT A THING!

THANK YOU LADIES, AND COME AGAIN!

WHAT WERE YOU DOING?

LEAVING A TIP.

CLICK CLI- CLICK

THAT WASN'T AS MUCH FUN AS LAST TIME.

♫ ... WHEN I WAS TWENTY-ONE ... IT WAS A VERY GOOD YEAR ... ♫

"GHOST WORLD"

THERE HE IS, AS ALWAYS...

POP!

MEAT IS MURDER

HAVE YOU EVER NOTICED THAT GUY?

I KNOW... THAT BUS LINE GOT RE-ROUTED LIKE FIVE YEARS AGO!

I ALWAYS CALL HIM "NORMAN"

WHY?

...BECAUSE OF NORMAN KNAEGEL?

NO... EWW, NO WAY!

NO, BECAUSE OF THAT NORMAN...

DON'T YOU JUST LOVE THE IDEA OF SOME LITTLE KID DOING THAT? IT'S SO RETARDED AND EGOMANIACAL!

NORMAN NORMAN NORMAN NORMAN NORMAN NORMAN NORMAN NORMAN NORMAN NORMAN NORMAN

IT SEEMS LIKE SOMETHING YOU WOULD DO!

BREAKFA T LUNCH

Angel's

47.

48.

WE'LL **KILL OURSELVES** IF WE NEVER DO THIS···

WHAT ARE YOU GOING TO SAY?

SHH, IT'S RINGING!

BOOOOPP EEEP THE NUMBER YOU HAVE REACHED HAS BEEN DISCONNECTED OR IS NO LONGER IN SERVICE···

UH-OH···

WHAT?

I THOUGHT YOU DECIDED YOU **HATED** ANGEL'S···

ONLY BECAUSE THAT **FUCKING BITCH** AND HER FRIENDS ARE ALWAYS THERE··· I'M NOT **ABOUT** TO LET **THEM** RUIN IT···

WE SHOULD FIGURE OUT SOME WAY TO GET MELORRA AND **JOSH** TOGETHER··· THEY WOULD TOTALLY **HATE** EACH OTHER!

THAT'S CRUEL AND INHUMAN PUNISHMENT!

I FEEL SORRY FOR JOSH; ONE OF US SHOULD FUCK HIM···

YOU SHOULD. HE OBVIOUSLY LIKES YOU BETTER.

NO HE DOESN'T! HE **HATES** ME! HE **LOVES** YOU!

NO **WAY**, I'M LIKE HIS LITTLE PAL! I'M SURE YOU'RE HIS TOTAL **DREAM GIRL!** I **GUARANTEE** HE THINKS ABOUT YOU WHEN HE JERKS OFF **WAY MORE** THAN ME!

I THOUGHT YOU SAID HE DIDN'T JERK OFF!

ALL GUYS JERK OFF!

HEY LOOK!

OH MY GOD, IS THAT MRS. SATANIST?

JOINT CUSTODY TUE WED THU

MOT

WHY IS SHE ALL ALONE?

SHH! C'MON!

WHERE'S HE AT?

HE'S IN FLORIDA AND HE CAN **STAY THERE** FOR ALL I CARE!

EXCUSE ME, DEAR... **ARE YOU IN LINE?**

ADULT 5 00
CHILD 3 00 UNDER 12

I PROMISE I WON'T GO TO COLLEGE.

IT JUST OCCURRED TO ME -- WHERE'S **NORMAN?**

MIK

MOSS

HEY LOOK! THEY **RE-ACTIVATED** THIS BUS STOP!

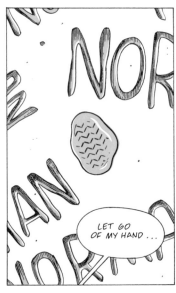

NOR

IAN

LET GO OF MY HAND...

I CAN'T FIGURE OUT WHAT'S GOING ON IN THIS ONE...

YEAH, WHAT THE FUCK?

GOD, YOU'RE RIGHT ABOUT THIS ALBUM!

I KNOW, I CAN'T BELIEVE I FINALLY FOUND IT AFTER ALL THESE YEARS!

LOOK AT THIS! I TOOK THIS WHEN I WAS LIKE EIGHT!

GOD, HOW LONG HAS THAT GRAFITTI BEEN THERE?

I KNOW!

IT'S SO WEIRD THAT YOU TOOK A PICTURE OF YOUR GARAGE!

GHOST WORLD

I CAN'T EVEN LOOK AT THESE PICTURES FROM SIXTH GRADE!

EW, WAIT! IS THAT MELORRA?

YUP, AND NAOMI... THE JUNIOR JAPS OF AMERICA!

SHE WAS ALWAYS SUPER UGLY!

LOOK, IT'S JOANIE... LOOK HOW BEAUTIFUL SHE WAS...

WAIT, WHICH ONE WAS SHE?

THE SECOND WIFE -- THE NICE ONE... GOD, LOOK AT HER...

EW, AND THERE'S THE BITCH...

I REMEMBER HER... WAS SHE THE THIRD OR FOURTH WIFE?

THERE WAS NO FOURTH WIFE!

GOD, LOOK AT HER... WHAT A FUCKING **MONSTER!**

NICE HOOTERS, THOUGH.

LOOK... THAT WAS BACK WHEN I HATED YOU...

I REMEMBER **EVERYTHING** ABOUT THAT PARTY... I REMEMBER I GOT A **PLASTIC CANTEEN** FOR A PRIZE!

MY DAD MUST HAVE PICKED THAT OUT...

OH **CUTE!** LOOK AT ME!

WHAT A LITTLE **HOSEBAG!**

SHUT UP! I WAS TOTALLY **ADORABLE!**

GOD, I REMEMBER THAT RECORD-- I USED TO PLAY THAT LIKE A **HUNDRED TIMES** EVERY DAY!

♫ I'VE GOT A SMILE ON MY FACE AND A RI-BBON SOMETHING SOMETHING ♫ ...A RI-BBON FOR MY HAIR... ♫

...I CAN'T REMEMBER, BUT IT WAS TOTALLY AMAZING!

WHATEVER HAPPENED TO ALL MY OLD RECORDS?

TSK!

CLACK CLACK

CLACK CLACK

CLACK CLACK CLACK

GOD, NO WONDER KIDS ARE SO SCREWED-UP TODAY-- THESE CHILDREN'S RECORDS ARE TOTALLY **CREEPY!** THIS GUY LOOKS LIKE A **CHILD MOLESTER!**

YOU'LL NEVER FIND IT HERE...

IF I DON'T FIND THAT RECORD I'LL BE LACHRYMOSE!

YOU'LL WHAT?

OH SHIT!!

56.

HAS HE EVER EVEN HAD A GIRLFRIEND? MAYBE HE **IS** GAY...

YEAH, I DUNNO... I GUESS IT'S POSSIBLE... IT'S MORE LIKE HE'S **ASEXUAL**...

IT'S SO HARD TO TELL WITH HIM... HE'S SUCH A TACITURN FELLOW...

WHERE DID YOU GET ALL THESE WORDS?

OH, IT'S JUST BECAUSE OF STUDYING FOR THAT STUPID TEST MY DAD WANTS ME TO TAKE...

I THOUGHT YOU WEREN'T GOING TO TAKE THAT TEST.

YEAH, WELL... MY DAD ALREADY PAID FOR IT, AND HE'S REALLY BEEN PESTERING ME AND EVERYTHING... IT'S A TOTAL DRAG...

YOU ARE SUCH A FUCKING LIAR.

I'M **NOT** LYING, I JUST--

YOU TELL ME EVERY **STUPID DETAIL** OF YOUR LIFE BUT YOU DON'T EVEN **MENTION** THAT YOU'RE STUDYING FOR THIS TEST?

THAT'S BECAUSE YOU'RE ACTING LIKE SUCH A **CREEP** ABOUT IT -- I'M ONLY TAKING A STUPID **TEST**!

MAYBE I'M JUST **SICK** OF PUTTING MORE INTO THIS FRIENDSHIP THAN I GET OUT OF IT...

WHAT THE FUCK ARE YOU **TALKING** ABOUT!?

LIKE HOW COME **I'M** ALWAYS THE ONE WHO HAS TO CALL YOU? YOU **NEVER** CALL ME...

YOU'RE OUT OF YOUR MIND! I CALLED YOU **TODAY!** PRACTICALLY EVERYTHING YOU'VE EVER **DONE** IS BECAUSE OF ME! I FEEL LIKE I PRACTICALLY HAVE TO **TELL YOU** WHAT TO DO!

57.

OH, BECAUSE YOU'RE **SO MUCH** MORE INTERESTING AND **SO MUCH** SMARTER THAN ME...

WELL IF I'M SUCH A **JERK** WHY DO YOU HANG OUT WITH ME?

WHO KNOWS...

LOOK, WHY ARE YOU **SO FREAKED OUT?** BECAUSE OF THE **ONE PERCENT CHANCE** THAT I MIGHT **POSSIBLY** GO TO COLLEGE?!

NO, BECAUSE YOU'RE ACTING SO **WEIRD** ABOUT IT! WHAT IS IT, SOME BIG **SECRET?!** IT'S LIKE YOU'RE TRYING TO **SNEAK AWAY** OR SOMETHING...

THAT'S JUST BECAUSE **YOU'RE** ACTING SO WEIRD!

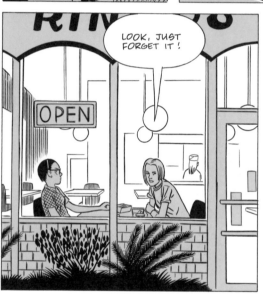

LOOK, JUST FORGET IT!

OPEN

GOD, I GOT INTO THIS BIG ARGUMENT WITH JOHN ELLIS YESTERDAY...

MM.

HE ALWAYS ACCUSES ME OF TRYING TO LOOK 'COOL'... I WAS LIKE, "EVERYBODY **TRIES** TO LOOK COOL, I JUST HAPPEN TO BE **SUCCESSFUL**..." WHAT, DOES HE THINK THAT MOST PEOPLE ARE TRYING TO LOOK **BAD?**

IT'S NO WONDER HE DOESN'T HAVE ANY FRIENDS... EVERYTHING ABOUT HIM IS TOTALLY **CONTENTIOUS**...

GOD, **FUCK YOU!**

WHAT?! WHAT THE FUCK IS **WRONG** WITH YOU!?

YOU ARE!

"OH, HE'S SO CONTENTIOUS"

JESUS!

THAT'S NOT EVEN ONE OF MY STUDY WORDS! WHY ARE YOU ACTING LIKE SUCH AN **INSANE PSYCHO**!?!

HAVE FUN IN COLLEGE.

≡ S O B ≡

≡ SOB ≡

GOD, FUCK YOU BITCH!

KIDDO? WHAT'S WRONG?

≡ SNIFF ≡

DO YOU KNOW WHERE ALL MY OLD RECORDS ARE?

DUMPLING, IF THERE'S SOMETHING WRONG I WISH YOU'D TELL ME...

IT'S NOTHING... IT'S JUST SOME HORMONAL THING...

I HAVE TO GO OUT FOR AWHILE AND GET SOME TAMPONS.

≡ SOB ≡

WHAT **ABOUT** HER, ASSHOLE?

WHAT SHOW ARE YOU GOING ON?

THE "SUNNY SUMMERS SHOW."

I NEVER EVEN HEARD OF IT!

THAT'S BECAUSE IT'S ON "THE FRIENDSHIP NETWORK"...

TUESDAY AT TEN O'CLOCK!

WHO DO WE KNOW WHO HAS CABLE?

EVERYBODY, BUT YOU HAVE TO PAY EXTRA FOR THE FRIENDSHIP CHANNEL...

WHY WOULD SOMEONE LIKE YOU EVEN **HAVE** CABLE?

IT'S FREE WITH THE BUILDING...

HOW CAN YOU STAND THERE AND SAY THAT?

DO I LOOK LIKE I'M STANDING?

HOW DO YOU KNOW THIS GUY?

HOW **DO** WE KNOW HIM?

DON'T ASK ME!

BOOOOO

...THAT'S **RIGHT**, I **DON'T** CARE ABOUT THOSE KIDS, AND IF·· YEAH,YEAH, YEAH **SHUT UP, RETARD!** IF ANY OF YOU **IDIOTS** CARED YOU'D MAKE SURE THE CATHOLIC CHUR·· **HEY! SHU-**

LET HIM FINISH!

BEEEP BEEP

"CHUCK" CHILD-MOLESTER'S FRIEND

LET ME GUESS·· THIS GUY IS OBSESSED WITH SERIAL KILLERS, CIRCUS FREAKS, GUNS, NAZIS...

YEAH, E**X**ACTLY!

...HOW DO YOU FEEL ABOUT HIM?

ALL OF HIS "OFFENSIVE" OPINIONS ARE SO **CONTRIVED** IT'S HARD TO TAKE HIM SERIOUSLY··· IT'S JUST A CHEAP, EASY WAY TO GET ATTENTION!

EXACTLY! HE'S TOTALLY JUST A **PATHETIC PUSSY** WHOSE MOMMY DIDN'T LOVE HIM ENOUGH!

SHH!

I ACTUALLY WANT TO HEAR THIS!

THAT'S IT... COVER YOUR BRAKE... SLOWLY... PRESSING... PRESSING... COMPLETE STOP... PERFECT!

NOW WHAT?

PARK, IGNITION, WINDOWS, LOCK.

WHERE HAVE YOU BEEN ALL MY LIFE, ENID?

SO WHAT DO YOU THINK, DUANE--CAN I PASS MY TEST?

IF I WAS ALLOWED TO, I'D **GUARANTEE** IT!

LOOK, I'M GIVING YOU **ANOTHER** DOUBLE SMILEY FACE! THAT'S THREE FOR THREE, ENID! **BRAVO!**

12

KA-SPLIT

...SO?

WHAT?

DO YOU WANT TO DO IT? I'LL DO MOST OF THE DRIVING...

IT'S JUST KIND OF WEIRD... I MEAN, YOUR **DAD** SHOULD DRIVE YOU TO COLLEGE, SHOULDN'T HE? HOW AM I SUPPOSED TO GET HOME?

BEGINNE LEAGU

I DUNNO... IT'S DO-ABLE...

WHAT KIND OF CAR ARE WE GETTING?

HI.

WHAT ARE YOU UP TO?

LIKE I SAID, THESE THINGS ARE GETTIN' HARDER TO FIND; NOW THEY USE VANS, I THINK··· BUT YOU COULD DO A LOT WORSE THAN THIS ONE, ESPECIALLY FOR A NEW DRIVER. SHE'S GOT UNBELIEVABLY LOW MILEAGE, AND IF YOU GET INTO AN ACCIDENT I **PROMISE** YOU'LL BE THE ONE WALKING AWAY!

YOU REALLY SHOULD THINK ABOUT THIS, PUMPKIN···IT'S LIABLE TO COST A LOT MORE THAN YOU THINK; YOU'RE GOING TO HAVE TO SPEND A **FORTUNE** ON GAS···

IT'S MY MONEY, ISN'T IT? CAN'T I DO WHAT I WANT JUST **ONCE** IN MY LIFE?

YOU'VE TRICKED ME INTO MOVING TWO THOUSAND MILES AWAY AND RUINING MY LIFE··· CAN'T YOU LET ME HAVE THIS ONE MORSEL OF FUN?

WHADDYA MEAN!? IT'S NOT "DEATH ROCK"! IT'S NOT EVEN **BLACK**!

I'M JUST SURPRISED···IT'S NOT REALLY YOUR STYLE···

YOU DON'T KNOW ME, JOSH.

APPARENTLY NOT.

···SO WHAT **IS** MY STYLE?

TO DEFY DEFINITION···

CAN YOU LET ME OUT UP HERE AT THE PEPPER MILL···

WHY? WHERE ARE YOU GOING?

NOWHERE IMPORTANT.

WHY ARE YOU MAD AT ME?

YOU WERE RIGHT, EVERYBODY **HATES** MY CAR...

BECKY SAID IT WAS A **GOTH DORKMOBILE**...

I HAVE NO IDEA WHAT THAT MEANS...

YEAH, WELL... WHATEVER...

WHERE ARE YOU GOING?

I'M GOING ON A DATE... GUESS WITH WHO...

WHO?

CAROL!

...NOT **THE** CAROL?

SHE'S DYING TO SEE YOU. I TOLD HER MAYBE SUNDAY...

YOU REMEMBER CAROL, DON'T YOU SWEETHEART?

WHAT THE FUCK ARE YOU **DOING?**

SO, WHAT AM I SUPPOSED TO SAY TO HER?

I KNOW, IT SUCKS... BUT I GUESS IT'S BETTER TO JUST NOT SAY ANYTHING...

I MEAN, SHE'LL BE GONE IN A MONTH ANYWAY...

YOU REALLY THINK SHE'S GOING?

I KNOW FOR A **FACT** SHE IS.

REALLY? I THOUGHT SHE WAS JUST...

JESUS CHRIST, I-I... THAT'S WEIRD...

I THOUGHT YOU DIDN'T CARE ABOUT HER AT ALL...

I DON'T, REALLY... I MEAN...

I'M JUST **SICK** OF IT! DEEP DOWN EVERY SINGLE BOY LIKES HER BETTER! THERE'S OBVIOUSLY SOMETHING **VERY WRONG** WITH ME THAT I DON'T KNOW ABOUT!

OH **NO** DEAR... THAT JUST ISN'T **TRUE**...

YOU'VE ALWAYS BEEN A VERY SWEET GIRL AND YOU'VE NEVER GIVEN ME A MINUTE OF TROUBLE... IT WOULD SUIT ME JUST FINE IF YOU STAYED HERE WITH ME FOR THE REST OF MY LIFE!

I-I GUESS I'M REALLY NOT SURE WHAT MY PLANS ARE YET...

DID I TELL YOU SHE BOUGHT A HEARSE?

A **HURST**?

A **HEARSE**. THE CAR THEY USE FOR FUNERALS...

OH MY GRACIOUS... **WHO** DID?

I HAVE TO GET BACK AND STUDY PRETTY SOON...

THAT'S OKAY, I JUST WANTED TO TELL YOU THAT I MIGHT BE COMING WITH YOU.

WHAT DO YOU MEAN? YOU'RE DRIVING ME TO STRATHMORE?

YEAH, EXCEPT I WAS THINKING MAYBE I'LL **MOVE** THERE AND LIVE WITH YOU AND GET A JOB AROUND THERE OR SOMETHING...

WHAT ARE YOU TALKING ABOUT?

I **KNEW** YOU DIDN'T WANT ME TO COME.

NO, NO... IT'S JUST WEIRD... I GUESS I'VE GOTTEN SO USED TO THE IDEA OF BEING ALONE, IT'S LIKE... I DUNNO...

YOU MAY NOW REST YOUR PENCILS.

I WAS HOPING TO GET A CHANCE TO LEARN ABOUT THE **GROWN-UP** ENID... AFTER ALL, I HAD **SOME** SMALL PART IN HOW YOU TURNED OUT!

YEAH, WELL, BECKY AND I ARE GOING ON A PRACTICE TRIP UP NORTH, SO I'M KIND OF IN A HURRY...

NOW WHERE AGAIN ARE YOU GOING?

CAVETOWN, USA... DON'T YOU REMEMBER? YOU AND JOANIE TOOK ME THERE WHEN YOU WERE MARRIED.

SOMEHOW IT FAILS TO REGISTER...

IT'S LIKE MY **ONLY** HAPPY MEMORY OF CHILDHOOD!

71.

WHY IS THIS GOING TO BE FUN AGAIN?

WE'RE HURTLING BACK IN TIME TO A **SAVAGE ERA** WHERE **DINOSAURS RULE THE EARTH!**

"HURTLING"? WAS THAT ON YOUR TEST?

BLOW ME!

SO WHAT'S IT LIKE AROUND STRATH-MORE?

IT'S PRETTY HOR-RIBLE... IT'S IN THE MIDDLE OF THIS SUPER-HORRIBLE NEIGHBORHOOD... IT SAID THERE WERE LIKE 150 RAPES LAST YEAR...

WHERE DID IT SAY THAT?

I DUNNO... IN LIKE SOME NEWSLETTER THEY SENT WITH THE CATALOG...

LOOK! THIRTEEN MILES! THIS IS SO **EASY!** WHY DON'T PEOPLE GO ON TRIPS LIKE THIS ALL THE TIME?

DO YOU REMEMBER MARK RUBIN?

CAVETOW USA 13 MI.

YEAH, TOTALLY...

HE WAS THE ONLY BOY WHO EVER LIKED ME MORE THAN YOU.

ALL I REMEMBER IS THAT HE ONCE POURED **TONS** OF KETCHUP ON HIS HOT DOG AND IT GROSSED ME OUT!

I REMEMBER THIS THING BEING **HUGE!**

GOD, IT'S TOTALLY **DESERTED**!

JESUS, LOOK AT THE SCARY HICKS THAT RUN THE PLACE... WE'RE DEFINITELY GOING TO BE THE VICTIMS IN SOME BIZARRE SATANIC RITUAL!

I KNOW... IT'S LIKE THE MANSON FAMILY RANCH!

OH MY GOD, I REMEMBER BEING SO **FREAKED OUT** BY THIS GUY...

GOD, I'M HAVING A **SEMI-RELIGIOUS EXPERIENCE**!

... MAYBE I SHOULDN'T GO WITH YOU...

IT'S KIND OF **SICK** TO FOLLOW YOU LIKE THAT...

GOD, IT'S REALLY PRETTY **SAD** WHEN YOU THINK ABOUT IT...

YEAH, I DON'T EXACTLY KNOW WHAT TO THINK ABOUT IT... IT ALL SEEMS KIND OF UNHEALTHY...

YEAH, BUT THEN AGAIN IF WE WERE SEPARATED IT MIGHT BE SO **HORRIBLE**...

I GUESS IT IS KIND OF CREEPY TO THINK OF US ACTING LIKE THIS WHEN WE'RE THIRTY...

THAT'S THE THING... I MEAN, REALLY WE'RE JUST LIKE TEENAGE FRIENDS... IT'S NOT LIKE WE'RE MARRIED OR SOMETHING... I MEAN, WE CAN ALWAYS BE FRIENDS... WE DON'T HAVE TO LIVE TOGETHER AND STUFF...

GOD...

YOU KNOW WHAT I MEAN...

YEAH, BUT IN A WAY I DON'T SEE ANYTHING WRONG WITH US ALWAYS STAYING TOGETHER...

SOMETIMES I WONDER IF MAYBE I REALLY **AM** A LESBO...

I MEAN, DON'T WORRY OR ANYTHING...

LOOK AT THIS DORKY HICK NEWSCASTER... I WONDER IF HE HAS TO WORK AT LIKE A HARDWARE STORE DURING THE DAY...

NewsCenter 440

THIS IS SO DEPRESSING...

WHAT?

JUST HOW EVERYTHING IS ALL THE SAME NO MATTER WHERE YOU GO...

CAN'T YOU AT LEAST BE DEPRESSED ABOUT ME...

LOOK, I DIDN'T SAY YOU COULDN'T COME WITH ME... I JUST FEEL WEIRD ABOUT IT... YOU CAN STILL COME...

OH YEAH, YOU REALLY WANT ME TO...

WHAT? I DO!

WELL MAYBE I DON'T! I DON'T WANT TO GO ANYWHERE OR DO ANYTHING... I JUST WANT IT TO BE LIKE IT WAS IN HIGH SCHOOL!

PACO'S

I GUESS THAT'S THE PROBLEM... I FEEL LIKE I WANT TO BECOME A TOTALLY DIFFERENT PERSON...

I DON'T GET WHAT THAT HAS TO DO WITH ME...

IT HAS EVERYTHING TO DO WITH YOU... YOU REMEMBER EVERY LITTLE DETAIL I WISH I COULD FORGET...

...BEFORE I WAS GOING TO COLLEGE, MY SECRET PLAN WAS TO ONE DAY NOT TELL ANYBODY AND JUST GET ON SOME BUS TO SOME RANDOM CITY AND JUST MOVE THERE AND BECOME THIS TOTALLY DIFFERENT PERSON...

THEN WHAT?

74.

...AND NOT COME BACK UNTIL I HAD TOTALLY BECOME THIS NEW PERSON... I USED TO THINK ABOUT IT ALL THE TIME...

I DON'T GET IT...

THAT'S BECAUSE YOU DON'T **UTTERLY LOATHE** YOURSELF...

MAIL CALL, KIDDO.

UH-OH...

WHAT SEE A MAN

I TOLD YOU I WASN'T SMART ENOUGH TO PASS THAT TEST.

I THINK YOU FORGOT MY COOKIES.

THEY'RE IN THE BAG.

BAGEL SPACE

HI.

OH, HI... I DIDN'T EVEN SEE YOU...

WHAT'S WRONG?

I THINK THERE'S SOMETHING WRONG WITH MY EYES... YOU'RE ALL BLURRY...

I THOUGHT FOR SURE YOU WERE GOING TO SAY "NO SHIT, SHERLOCK!" TO THAT GUY...

GIVE ME A LARGE ORANGE JUICE...

ACTUALLY, HE'S A REALLY NICE GUY... GOD, YOU'RE FADING IN AND OUT...

SOME LADY LEFT WITHOUT HER BAGEL... DO YOU WANT IT?

NAH, YOUR BAGELS ARE TOO WASPY.

HEY ENID, WHAT'S UP?

OH... HEY JOSH!

SO, ARE YOU ALMOST DONE?

YEAH, I'M ALL PUNCHED OUT... LET'S GO...

77.

WELL HOW ARE YOU?

DO YOU REMEMBER ME?

OH SURE!

GOD, I THOUGHT MAYBE SOMETHING HAPPENED TO YOU!

DO YOU SEE ANYTHING?

I'M GETTING A VERY POWERFUL IMAGE...

SO WHAT'S MY FUTURE?

I SEE A WOMAN...

IT'S THE 1930'S, I BELIEVE... TWENTIES OR THIRTIES... I GET THE SENSE THAT SHE'S AN ARTIST OF SOME KIND, OR A SCHOLAR... A WOMAN OF INTELLECT AND LEISURE ...A SEXUAL LIBERTINE...

SHE HAS A HAUNTED QUALITY, AS THOUGH SHE WANTS TO TELL YOU SOMETHING... I SEE A ROAD AHEAD WITH MANY FORKS, ALL OF WHICH LEAD, IT SEEMS, TO GLOOM AND DARKNESS... SHE HESITATES...

...AND?

I'M LOSING HER... SHE'S RUNNING AWAY...

WAIT... NO, THAT'S IT.

SO WHAT DOES IT ALL MEAN?

AS I TOLD YOU, THIS IS JUST AN INTRODUCTORY PSYCHIC IMPRESSION... TO GET ANY **REAL** DATA WE'RE GOING TO HAVE TO DO A FULL ASTROLOGICAL RUNDOWN...

YOU'VE GROWN INTO A VERY BEAUTIFUL YOUNG WOMAN.

THE END

Daniel Clowes